A Swimmer's Day

Written by Charlotte Middleton

Linda wakes up.

It is time for breakfast.

After breakfast,
Linda goes for a jog.

Then she goes
in the swimming pool.

splash!

She swims up and down,
up and down.

⑧

After swimming,
Linda rides her bike.

It is time for lunch.

After lunch,
Linda goes to the gym.

She jumps up and down, up and down.

It is time for dinner.

⑬

What does Linda do after dinner?

Jog?

Swim?

Ride?   Jump?

No! It is time to rest.

16